THE
HOLE
IN OUR
GOSPEL

WHAT DOES GOD EXPECT OF US?

THE
HOLE
IN OUR
GOSPEL

THE ANSWER THAT CHANGED MY LIFE AND MIGHT JUST
CHANGE THE WORLD

STUDY GUIDE

RICHARD STEARNS

THOMAS NELSON
Since 1798

NASHVILLE   MEXICO CITY   RIO DE JANEIRO

Published in Nashville, Tennessee, by W Publishing, an imprint of Thomas Nelson. Thomas Nelson is a registered trademark of HarperCollins Christian Publishing, Inc.

Author is represented by the literary agency of Alive Communications, Inc., 7680 Goddard Street, Suite 200, Colorado Springs, CO 80920, www.alivecommunications.com.

Unless otherwise indicated, Scripture quotations are taken from the Holy Bible, New International Version®, NIV®. Copyright © 1973, 1978, 1984, 2011 by Biblica, Inc.™ Used by permission of Zondervan. All rights reserved worldwide. www.zondervan.com.

Scriptures marked NKJV are taken from the NEW KING JAMES VERSION®. © 1982 by Thomas Nelson, Inc. Used by permission. All rights reserved.

Scriptures marked MSG are taken from The Message by Eugene H. Peterson. © 1993, 1994, 1995, 1996, 2000, 2001, 2002. Used by permission of NavPress Publishing Group.

Italics added to Scripture quotations are the author's own emphasis. In some cases, names and locations have been changed to protect the privacy of individuals whose stories are told in these pages.

At the author's request, all royalties due to the author will benefit World Vision's work with children in need.

ISBN 978-0-7180-3760-4

Printed in the United States of America

14 15 16 17 18 RRD 6 5 4 3 2 1

CONTENTS

HOW TO USE THIS STUDY GUIDE

Christ has no body now on earth but yours,
no hands but yours, no feet but yours.
Yours are the eyes through which
Christ's compassion for the world is to look out;
yours are the feet with which He is to go about doing good;
and yours are the hands with which He is to bless us now.

Saint Teresa of Avila

In 1998, Richard (Rich) Stearns got a telephone call that changed his life. The contented corporate CEO was asked to consider becoming CEO of World Vision U.S., a Christian humanitarian organization. He said no thank you and did everything he could to get out of taking the job. However, eventually he came to believe that there was a hole in his understanding of the gospel and that God wanted to fill that hole. God was asking for more than belief, more than church attendance, more than prayer and Bible study. He was asking Rich for *everything*—a total life commitment and partnership with God and God's people in changing the world.

The Hole in Our Gospel is Rich's story of what he came to believe the whole gospel is, what he did about it, and what God is asking of the rest of his Church. *The Hole in Our Gospel Study Guide* offers an opportunity for you to spend six sessions studying the book with a small group, exploring the question, "What does God expect of us, of me?"

PRE-SESSION PREPARATION

Each study session begins with preparation for you to do before your group meets. You'll see the chapters of *The Hole in Our Gospel* that you should read and find short excerpts from the book along with questions for you to answer. (Note that the page numbers in this guide correspond to the special edition published in 2014.) Write your thoughts in the blank space provided. If you need more space, use a separate notebook. If your time is limited, you can participate in the group meeting without answering the questions beforehand, but you will get more out of the discussion if you take time to prepare. At a minimum, read the chapters of the book.

If the stories and ideas in the book make you uncomfortable or challenge the status quo of your life, be honest about where you are struggling or even how you disagree. Resist the temptation to shut down or leave the group if the content hits close to home. Keep asking God to reveal what he expects of you—uniquely you, the way he designed you. It takes courage to examine your life and admit where there are gaps between what you believe and how you are living, but this is not an invitation to shame. Instead, it is an invitation to open your heart to God's love. Knowing this love is the heart of the gospel, because knowing this love changes everything.

GROUP DISCUSSION

You will find instructions for how to guide your small-group discussion time under the heading "Group Discussion." The group members will spend the core of that time discussing the questions they answered during the pre-session preparation. The group leader may select certain questions rather than covering all of them. The important thing is to have an honest and fruitful discussion about the book chapters.

During your discussion, you may find it helpful to have someone read aloud the excerpts from the book. Do read aloud the Bible passages before you discuss them. In addition, keep in mind a few ground rules that will make your group a valuable place for you to process what you are learning:

- Work to make the group a safe place. That means being honest about your thoughts and feelings as well as listening carefully to everyone else's.
- Resist the temptation to "fix" someone else's problem or to correct someone else's theology.
- Keep everything your group shares confidential.

These ground rules will foster a rewarding sense of community in your group and give God's Spirit a powerful forum to guide, equip, and send you out to be Christ's hands and feet in the world.

LIVING THE WORD

The "Living the Word" section follows the discussion time and will offer ideas for the group to act on what they've learned. The group leader should allow time for the group to look over "Living the Word" and talk about what they want to do.

There is a place in this section for you to jot down some notes about what you decided to do and how it went. Beginning in session 2, you will have a chance to check in with your group about what you learned from the previous week's activity. During this check-in time, you will be asked to share your experiences as well as to listen to those of your fellow group members. However, don't worry if you don't have time to do the activity one week or are just joining the study. Hearing what others have learned will be nourishment enough on its own.

> If you are a group leader, there are additional resources for you at the back of this guide.

YOU LACK ONE THING

The word *gospel* literally means "good news." Jesus declared that he had come to "preach good news to the poor" (Luke 4:18). But what good news, what gospel did the Church have for Richard and his brothers in Rakai?

The Hole in Our Gospel, *p. xxviii*

OBJECTIVES

- To consider whether we have had a limited idea of the gospel

- To consider the urgency of fixing this truncated gospel in a suffering world

PRE-SESSION PERSONAL STUDY

To prepare for this session, read the introduction, prologue, and chapters 1 through 3 of *The Hole in Our Gospel*. Meditate on the following quotes from the book and the Bible and answer the related questions. (This same format will repeat in each pre-session of the guide. Use the space provided or a separate notebook to record your responses.)

> More and more, our view of the gospel has been narrowed to a simple transaction, marked by checking a box on a bingo card at some prayer breakfast, registering a decision for Christ, or coming forward during an altar call. I have to admit that my own view of evangelism, based on the Great Commission, amounted to just that for many years. It was about saving as many people from hell as possible—for the *next* life. It minimized any concern for those same people in *this* life. It wasn't as important that they were poor or hungry or persecuted, or perhaps rich, greedy, and arrogant; we just had to get them to pray the "sinner's prayer," and then we'd move on to the next potential convert. *(p. 5)*

1. In what ways has your view of the gospel emphasized getting yourself and other people saved for the next life? What are the signs of this emphasis in what you've said and done? In what your church says and does?

2. In what ways, if any, has your view of the gospel minimized concern for people's circumstances in this life? What are the signs of this minimization in what you haven't said and done? In what your church doesn't say and do? In how money and time are spent?

Picture for a moment your neighbor's son's being asked to speak at the Sunday service at your church. Can you imagine your shock if he stood up, read the Scripture pertaining to the second coming of Christ, and then said, "Today this scripture is fulfilled in your hearing"? That is exactly what Jesus did in the synagogue in Nazareth, except he referred to the Messiah's first coming. This happened at the very start of Jesus' public ministry, immediately after his baptism by John the Baptist and the forty days in the wilderness, facing the temptations of Satan. Listen to this remarkable passage:

> Jesus returned to Galilee in the power of the Spirit, and news about him spread through the whole countryside. He was teaching in their synagogues, and everyone praised him.
>
> He went to Nazareth, where he had been brought up, and on the Sabbath day he went into the synagogue, as was his custom. He stood up to read, and the scroll of the prophet Isaiah was handed to him. Unrolling it, he found the place where it is written:
>
> "The Spirit of the Lord is on me,
>   because he has anointed me
>   to proclaim good news to the poor.
> He has sent me to proclaim freedom for the prisoners
>   and recovery of sight for the blind,
> to set the oppressed free,
>   to proclaim the year of the Lord's favor."
>
> Then he rolled up the scroll, gave it back to the attendant and sat down. The eyes of everyone in the synagogue were fastened on him. He began by saying to them, "Today this scripture is fulfilled in your hearing."
> (Luke 4:14–21)

The passage Jesus read was a prophecy that envisioned a future messiah who would be both a king and a servant. As perhaps Jesus' first public statement of his identity as the Messiah, what he said in Nazareth was a declaration both of who he was and why he had come. It was in essence Jesus' *mission statement*, and it laid out the great promises of God to those who receive the Messiah and his coming kingdom. In this mission statement, we see three main components. *(pp. 8–9)*

3. Rich goes on in *The Hole in Our Gospel* to list these three components of Jesus' mission statement:

    • Proclamation of the good news of salvation

    • Compassion for the sick and sorrowful

    • Commitment to justice

    Reread Jesus' mission statement in Luke 4:14–21 and underline where you see the proclamation of the good news of salvation of souls. Now put an arrow where you see compassion for the poor, sick, and sorrowful, and an arrow where you see a commitment to justice. Do those three components seem like an accurate breakdown of Jesus' mission statement? Do you think Jesus is only talking about sight for the spiritually blind and freedom for the spiritually oppressed? Explain.

Two crude piles of stones just outside the door mark the graves of Richard's parents. It disturbs me that he must walk past them every day. He and his brothers must have watched first their father and then their mother die slow and horrible deaths. I wondered if the boys were the ones who fed them and bathed them in their last days. Whatever the case, Richard, a child himself, is now the head of his household. *(p. xxvii)*

4. How does this story from the prologue of Richard, the boy orphaned by AIDS, affect you?

I much preferred living in my bubble, the one that, until that moment, had safely contained my life, family, and career. It kept difficult things like this out, insulating me from anything too raw or upsetting. When such things intruded, as they rarely did, a channel could be changed, a newspaper page turned, or a check written to keep the poor at a safe distance. But not in Rakai. There, "such things" had faces and names—even my name, Richard. *(p. xxv)*

5. In what ways, if any, do you relate to Rich's desire to keep the poor at a safe distance? What fears or other feelings perpetuate this desire?

Bob Pierce, the founder of World Vision, once prayed, "Let my heart be broken with the things that break the heart of God." But who *really* wants his heart broken? Is this something to ask of God? Don't we pray that God will *not* break our hearts? But as I look at the life of Jesus, I see that he was, as Isaiah described him, "a Man of sorrows . . . acquainted with grief" (53:3 NKJV). Jesus' heart was continually moved to compassion as he encountered the lame, the sick, the widow, and the orphan. *(p. xxvii)*

6. What would it feel like to have your heart broken with the things that break God's heart?

7. Do you think you need that? Why or why not?

What good is it, my brothers and sisters, if someone claims to have faith but has no deeds? Can such faith save them? Suppose a brother or a sister is without clothes and daily food. If one of you says to them, "Go in peace; keep warm and well fed," but does nothing about their physical needs, what good is it? In the same way, faith by itself, if it is not accompanied by action, is dead.

But someone will say, "You have faith; I have deeds."

Show me your faith without deeds, and I will show you my faith by my deeds. You believe that there is one God. Good! Even the demons believe that—and shudder.

You foolish person, do you want evidence that faith without deeds is useless? Was not our father Abraham considered righteous for what he did when he offered his son Isaac on the altar? You see that his faith and his actions were working together, and his faith was made complete by what he did. And the scripture was fulfilled that says, "Abraham believed God, and it was credited to him as righteousness," and he was called God's friend. You see that a person is considered righteous by what they do and not by faith alone.

In the same way, was not even Rahab the prostitute considered righteous for what she did when she gave lodging to the spies and sent them off in a different direction? As the body without the spirit is dead, so faith without deeds is dead. *(James 2:14–26)*

8. In this passage, what reasons does James give for critiquing a type of "faith" not expressed in deeds?

9.	Do you believe faith without deeds is dead? Why or why not? Can there be genuine saving faith in Christ that is not expressed in the ways we treat others?

For it is by grace you have been saved, through faith—and this is not from yourselves, it is the gift of God—not by works, so that no one can boast. For we are God's handiwork, created in Christ Jesus to do good works, which God prepared in advance for us to do. *(Ephesians 2:8–10)*

10.	How does this passage in Ephesians complement or contradict James 2:14–26? What role for deeds does Paul give (see verse 10)?

11. Some would say that Christians have used Ephesians 2:8–9 to justify treating faith as simply a state of mind or the result of a one-time prayer. Do you agree or disagree with this criticism? Explain your answer.

"Are you willing to be open to God's will for your life?"

Ouch! What a terrible question to ask someone. What a *rude* question to ask someone! And what an uncomfortable question for someone to answer.

That one question really put me at a loss for words. I think there was a long pause; then slowly I started to answer. "Well . . . yes . . . I *do* want to be open to God's will. But . . ." And, you see, as I thought about my answer, there were a lot of buts. *(p. 21)*

12. Ask yourself that question: "Are you willing to be open to God's will for your life?" What "buts" are there in your heart when you think about that question?

GROUP DISCUSSION

- Think of a time or place that completely overwhelmed you and forced you to think about life differently. Take about one minute to share something of that experience.

- Discuss your insights from the "Pre-Session Personal Study" questions. Your group leader will select the questions for discussion.

- Has our gospel had a hole in it? Explain your view. If your answer is yes, how urgent is it for us to fill that hole? Why?

- Read "Living the Word" below. Are there things you are already doing to put your faith into action? What might you do this week?

- How can the group pray for you? For example, are you ready to ask God to break your heart with the things that break his heart? Do you have questions, feelings, or concerns that you'd like to put before God regarding faith and deeds? Write down one another's requests for prayer.

- Take time to pray for one another. You might let each person pray for the person on his or her right. Or, if you prefer, have one person read the prayer requests, and then let the whole group finish your prayer time by saying together this popular version of the prayer Jesus taught his disciples to pray in the Sermon on the Mount (Matthew 6:9–13):

> Our Father in heaven,
> hallowed be your name,
> your kingdom come,
> your will be done,
>   on earth as it is in heaven.
> Give us today our daily bread.
> And forgive us our debts,
>   as we also have forgiven our debtors.
> And lead us not into temptation,
>   but deliver us from the evil one.
> For yours is the kingdom and the power
>   and the glory forever. Amen.

PERSONAL ACTIVITY

LIVING THE WORD

This week, look for a way to put your faith into action. Every day there are thousands of opportunities to reflect God's love. Maybe you will offer to watch your neighbor's children for the afternoon, volunteer at a local shelter, call someone you know who needs a friend, advocate for a child in need, or donate money to an organization that cares for the poor. The goal is to become a transformed person whose actions are a result of faith rather than trying to prove something to God or to the world.

It's normal to feel outside your comfort zone in your acts of compassion, but as you spend time with God and trust in his love, action will begin to naturally flow out of your faith. Write some notes about this experience below.

What did you do?

What did you learn or take away from this experience?

If you found it hard to make time for this, why do you think that is the case?

COMPASSION AND JUSTICE

If God only used perfect people, nothing would get done. God will use anybody if you're available.

Rick Warren

OBJECTIVES

- To appreciate the centrality of compassion and justice in biblical theology

- To consider what this theme has to do with our lives

To prepare for this session, read chapters 4 through 7 of *The Hole in Our Gospel*. Meditate on the following quotes from the book and the Bible and answer the related questions.

> We take it as foundational that God will always listen to our prayers, but this passage [Isaiah 58] suggests we should not expect God to listen to prayers offered by insincere hearts. So if God is *not* pleased with man's prayers and veneration, what *does* please him?
>
> > Is not this the kind of fasting I have chosen:
> > to loose the chains of injustice
> >   and untie the cords of the yoke,
> > to set the oppressed free
> >   and break every yoke?
> > Is it not to share your food with the hungry
> >   and to provide the poor wanderer with shelter—
> > when you see the naked, to clothe him,
> >   and not to turn away from your own flesh and blood?
> >   (vv. 6–7 NIV 1984) *(pp. 43–44)*

1. What would the "fasting" Isaiah describes above look like today?

2. Do we have any reason to believe that God is no longer interested in this kind of fasting? If so, what reasons? If not, why not?

Then your light will break forth like the dawn,
    and your healing will quickly appear;
then your righteousness will go before you,
    and the glory of the LORD will be your rear guard.
Then you will call, and the LORD will answer;
    you will cry for help, and he will say: Here am I.
If you do away with the yoke of oppression,
    with the pointing finger and malicious talk,
and if you spend yourselves in behalf of the hungry
    and satisfy the needs of the oppressed,
then your light will rise in the darkness,
    and your night will become like the noonday.
The Lord will guide you always;
    he will satisfy your needs in a sun-scorched land
and will strengthen your frame.
    You will be like a well-watered garden,
    like a spring whose waters never fail. *(Isaiah 58:8–11)*

3. According to this passage in Isaiah, what blessings does God promise to people who practice this kind of fasting?

When the Son of Man comes in his glory, and all the angels with him, he will sit on his glorious throne. All the nations will be gathered before him, and he will separate the people one from another as a shepherd separates the sheep from the goats. He will put the sheep on his right and the goats on his left.

Then the King will say to those on his right, "Come, you who are blessed by my Father; take your inheritance, the kingdom prepared for you since the creation of the world. For I was hungry and you gave me something to eat, I was thirsty and you gave me something to drink, I was a stranger and you invited me in, I needed clothes and you clothed me, I was sick and you looked after me, I was in prison and you came to visit me."

Then the righteous will answer him, "Lord, when did we see you hungry and feed you, or thirsty and give you something to drink? When did we see you a stranger and invite you in, or needing clothes and clothe you? When did we see you sick or in prison and go to visit you?"

The King will reply, "Truly I tell you, whatever you did for one of the least of these brothers and sisters of mine, you did for me."

Then he will say to those on his left, "Depart from me, you who are cursed, into the eternal fire prepared for the devil and his angels. For I was hungry and you gave me nothing to eat, I was thirsty and you gave me nothing to drink, I was a stranger and you did not invite me in, I needed clothes and you did not clothe me, I was sick and in prison and you did not look after me."

They also will answer, "Lord, when did we see you hungry or thirsty or a stranger or needing clothes or sick or in prison, and did not help you?"

He will reply, "Truly I tell you, whatever you did not do for one of the least of these, you did not do for me." *(Matthew 25:31–45)*

4. What strikes you about the scene Jesus describes in this passage in Matthew? How does it challenge your view of what it means to be a follower of Christ?

5. How often do you think about those around you as though they were Christ himself? How would this affect the way you treat people?

In summary, we see throughout both the Old and New Testaments the bright thread of God's concern for the poor and the marginalized. We see in Christ's dramatic announcement of his messianic identity and mission in Luke 4 that he came "to preach good news to the poor" (v. 18). We learn that Christ's criterion for determining the authenticity of someone's profession to follow him is whether he or she tangibly cared for those in need. And now we are told that when we do care for them, we are actually caring for Christ himself—his identity merged with the least and the last. There is no whole gospel without compassion and justice shown to the poor. It's that simple. *(p. 48)*

6. Are you persuaded by this summary of the bright thread throughout the Old and New Testaments? Why or why not?

7. What are the implications for you?

Their eyes were hollow and vacant—eyes that had seen unspeakable things. Their souls seemed dead. I could see no life in them. *Jesus in his most distressing disguise.* They had been captured by the Ugandan army, and now they were being brought to World Vision for help, for redemption, for healing. They had names, Michael and Joseph. Michael's left arm was withered, the result of a gunshot wound sustained before he was fully grown, in some fight. The LRA warned their child soldiers that they would be murdered by their own people if they ever tried to go home. They were even told that if they were taken to the Children of War Center run by World Vision, they would be poisoned—or worse. That is why these boys were terrified that day, stepping out of the car.

The forty other "children of war"—damaged souls all—surrounded them and began singing and clapping joyfully. These songs of praise to God, anthems of healing and forgiveness, were more beautiful than any choir of angels. Michael and Joseph were dumbstruck at this welcome, so different from what they had expected. *(pp. 49–50)*

8. How did the story of Michael and Joseph affect you? Where do you see the gospel in their story?

You are not restoring a great painting that's shortly going to be thrown on the fire. You are not planting roses in a garden that's about to be dug up for a building site. You are—strange though it may seem, almost as hard to believe as the resurrection itself—accomplishing something that will become in due course part of God's new world. Every act of love, gratitude, and kindness; every work of art or music inspired by the love of God and delight in the beauty of his creation; every minute spent teaching a severely handicapped child to read or to walk; every act of care and nurture, of comfort and support, for one's fellow human beings and for that matter one's fellow nonhuman creatures; and of course every prayer, all Spirit-led teaching, every deed that spreads the gospel, builds up the church, embraces and embodies holiness rather than corruption, and makes the name of Jesus honored in the world—all of this will find its way, through the resurrecting power of God, into the new creation that God will one day make. That is the logic of the mission of God. —N. T. Wright *(p. 57)*

9. In this quote, N.T. Wright says this world is not going to be scrapped when Jesus returns. Rather, he says, this world will be *redeemed* when Jesus returns, and everything worthwhile that we do here and now has eternal significance. How do these two understandings of what God will do when Jesus returns lead to very different ways of living now?

10. Do you find Wright's view persuasive? Why or why not?

One of the most powerful reasons we don't totally surrender our lives to Christ is that we don't want to sacrifice the things we possess; they have begun to possess us. These things can include our jobs, our material assets, our money, our communities, and our friends—even our families. We cling to them, often out of a desire for security, comfort, and happiness, even though we know in our hearts that we can only find real happiness by serving the Lord. Consequently, our things become idols. *(p. 75)*

11. Is there anything you cling to for security, comfort, status, or happiness? If so, what? (You can write this down and keep it private. You won't have to share it with your group unless you choose to do so.)

Discerning our unique calling is not always a simple thing. We need to be quiet enough to hear God's still, small voice. We must also faithfully read the Scriptures, pray diligently, follow the Lord's teachings, listen to wise friends who know us, and consistently make ourselves available to serve. Finally, we have to remain open to God's possibilities, always willing to take the outrageous risk and do the unpredictable thing. *(p. 78)*

12. What has God's still, small voice been saying to you through your study this week?

GROUP DISCUSSION

- Did you have a chance to put your faith into action in a practical way this week? If so, what did you do? What did you learn? If not, what is one thing that got in the way?

- Discuss your insights from the "Pre-Session Personal Study" questions. Your group leader will select the questions for discussion.

- Is justice just for peaceniks? Explain your view.

- Read "Living the Word" below. What part of Isaiah 58 or Matthew 25 might you choose to memorize?

- How can the group pray for you? For instance, would you like help to see the other people around you as if they are Christ himself? Do you need help to discern where you fit into God's work of justice and compassion? Are you having trouble reconciling teachings such as Matthew 25 with your understanding of the gospel? Write down each other's requests for prayer.

- Begin your prayer time with a period of silence in which you sit with your eyes closed and your palms open. Imagine that you're offering up to Jesus whatever gets in the way of your answering his call. It might be your job, a fear, insecurities, questions, or concerns for family members. Imagine your hands emptying as you give those things to Jesus so that you can receive from him whatever he desires to give you. Then pray for one another.

PERSONAL ACTIVITY

LIVING THE WORD

This week, choose a portion of one of the Bible passages you have studied (Isaiah 58:1–11 or Matthew 25:31–46), and commit it to memory. Write the passage on a piece of paper and post it where you will see it more than once during the day—such as on your computer, your car dashboard, or your refrigerator. Read it aloud a couple of times each day, and then look away or close your eyes and try to repeat it from memory. Spend enough time with it that it becomes part of your thought life. Memorizing scripture passages like this is an important way of shaping your mind to be Christlike.

As you repeat the verses back to yourself, be aware of thoughts that surface. Do your thoughts argue with the Bible passage, or rejoice in it, or try to change the subject? Do they needle you with the gap between the passage and your life? Do you find yourself drawn toward the words of the passage or pushed away?

Write some notes about your experience:

What passage did you choose?

What thoughts came up when you were thinking about the passage?

ONE HUNDRED CRASHING JET LINERS

Our desire is not that others might be relieved while you are hard pressed, but that there might be equality.

2 Corinthians 8:13

OBJECTIVE

- To understand the most critical issues facing the poor and how we can address them

To prepare for this session, read chapters 8 through 14 of *The Hole in Our Gospel*. Meditate on the following quotes from the book and the Bible and answer the related questions.

On one occasion an expert in the law stood up to test Jesus. "Teacher," he asked, "what must I do to inherit eternal life?"

"What is written in the Law?" he replied. "How do you read it?"

He answered, "'Love the Lord your God with all your heart and with all your soul and with all your strength and with all your mind'; and, 'Love your neighbor as yourself.'"

"You have answered correctly," Jesus replied. "Do this and you will live."

But he wanted to justify himself, so he asked Jesus, "And who is my neighbor?"

In reply Jesus said: "A man was going down from Jerusalem to Jericho, when he was attacked by robbers. They stripped him of his clothes, beat him and went away, leaving him half dead. A priest happened to be going down the same road, and when he saw the man, he passed by on the other side. So too, a Levite, when he came to the place and saw him, passed by on the other side. But a Samaritan, as he traveled, came where the man was; and when he saw him, he took pity on him. He went to him and bandaged his wounds, pouring on oil and wine. Then he put the man on his own donkey, brought him to an inn and took care of him. The next day he took out two denarii and gave them to the innkeeper. 'Look after him,' he said, 'and when I return, I will reimburse you for any extra expense you may have.'

"Which of these three do you think was a neighbor to the man who fell into the hands of robbers?"

The expert in the law replied, "The one who had mercy on him."
Jesus told him, "Go and do likewise." *(Luke 10:25–37)*

1. What is Jesus' point in this parable he tells in Luke? What does it say about us if we ask "who is my neighbor?" and hope for an answer that doesn't involve people far away?

We have become detached and indifferent toward the constant and repeated images of poverty and adversity that bombard us. In fact, our apathy has even earned its own term: *compassion fatigue.* But we *cannot* claim that we don't know our distant neighbor is in need—not anymore, not today. *(p. 88)*

2. What is "compassion fatigue"? Have you experienced it? If so, how has it affected what you do?

Our problem is that the plight of suffering children in a far-off land simply hasn't gotten *personal* for us. We may hear about them with sorrow, but we haven't really been able to look at them as if they were our own children. *(p. 94)*

3. What could help us see children suffering far away as if they were our own children?

If it is in our power to prevent something very bad from happening, without thereby sacrificing anything of comparable moral significance, we ought to do it. —Peter Singer *(p. 97)*

4. Do you agree or disagree with Peter Singer's ethical principle above? Why? What are the implications?

If they are poor in America, we reason, it must be because they don't work as hard as the rest of us or have made bad choices. We may think that the poor are lazy or stupid, even if we wouldn't say it aloud. When we think about the poor in places such as Africa or Southeast Asia, we may bring other stereotypes into play, perhaps racial or cultural. We may shake our heads at why this nationality or that race just can't seem to get their act together. We wonder why their governments are so ineffective, their leaders so incompetent or corrupt, and their economic development so weak. Or we may look at them paternalistically, feeling sorry for them as a parent would a helpless child. All of these biases are patronizing at best and prejudiced at worst; they lessen the human dignity of people created in God's image. If we are to see the poor as God sees them, we first have to repent of our judgmental attitudes and feelings of superiority. *(p. 103)*

5. What biases, if any, do you tend to have about the poor?

6. Think about your own children or yourself as a child. Imagine that they (or you) are chronically hungry to the point where their bodies and minds are stunted, are chronically sick, have to walk for hours to get clean water, have hours of chores or work each day, and are exposed to war or other violence. How would that affect their performance at school and their future work life? Which one of these problems do you think would hinder their school performance the most?

For most of the poorest people in the world, their hard work doesn't matter. They are trapped within social, cultural, political, and economic systems that do not reward their labor. The result of this entrenched futility is devastating to the human spirit. A person, no matter how gifted or determined, cannot escape the trap in which he finds himself. He has lost the one thing that every person needs to thrive: hope—hope that he will somehow overcome his circumstances, that tomorrow can be better than today, and that his children might someday have a better life than his. *(p. 105)*

7. How easy is it for you to believe that large numbers of people are trapped in systems that don't reward their labor? Why?

Now this was the sin of your sister Sodom: She and her daughters were arrogant, overfed and unconcerned; they did not help the poor and needy. *(Ezekiel 16:49)*

8. What does it say about God that he wiped Sodom off the map because her citizens were unconcerned about the poor?

As we gathered around the borehole well that World Vision had drilled several years earlier right next to the school, the school's headmaster told us that before the borehole he had just forty students. Now more than four hundred children attended the school! The difference? Before the water came to Gbum Gbum, the women and children had to spend about five hours each day fetching water from a waterhole several kilometers away. They would rise early, before dawn, making several trips throughout the day; they had no time or energy for school. Another man told me that before the well, children and adults alike were riddled with guinea worm disease (dracunculiasis) caused by parasitic nematodes found in contaminated water. These worms grow inside the body, sometimes up to three feet in length, and then when full-grown, burrow out through the skin, causing crippling pain and infection. Now the guinea worms were gone. *(p. 123)*

Malaria need not reap so grim a toll. Medicines are available that, when administered on a timely basis, can stop the progression of the disease and save lives. Spraying insecticides in mosquito breeding areas and inside houses can reduce the likelihood of being bitten. Perhaps one of the most effective interventions is the use of insecticide-treated bed nets, especially for the most vulnerable—children and pregnant women. At a cost of less than ten dollars, these simple nets can greatly reduce risk and provide years of protection for a family. *(p. 128)*

9.   Think about the solutions to the problems of clean water and malaria described above. How do these solutions affect the people involved?

10. How does it affect you to know that some problems of the poor are solvable with a little money and expertise?

The battle against AIDS, like that against malaria and tuberculosis, is a winnable war—*if* we are willing to take up the fight. Uganda's incidence of HIV infections in 1991 was 21 percent. Then Uganda's president, Yoweri Museveni, declared war on AIDS as a threat to Uganda's future and security. . . . The result was astounding. The incidence of HIV infections fell from 21 percent to less than 7 percent between 1991 and 2011 as people changed their sexual behaviors. *(p. 133)*

While microfinance can take many forms, typically loan groups of six or twelve people are formed in a community comprised of neighbors who know and are willing to vouch for one another. Each member develops a plan to create a livelihood relying on his or her own talents, networks, and access to resources, estimating the amount of money needed to launch or capitalize the businesses. In this model, the microfinance institution (often operated by a nonprofit, such as Opportunity International, World Vision, or CARE) then makes a loan to the loan group, who then lends to the individual. The idea is that if the individual fails to pay back the loan, the group is responsible for repaying it. This results in considerable peer pressure and accountability, but it also promotes mutual support and cooperation among group members. *(p. 137)*

11. What do you like about the way microfinance works?

We must face the brutal facts about poverty and injustice—only then can we take the first steps to respond. But the magnitude of the problems facing the poor can be overwhelming and can drive us away. That is why it is so critical to remember . . .

- Every one of these hurting people is created in God's image and loved by him.

- Every one of these challenges has a solution.

- Every one of us can make a difference. *(p. 144)*

12. How does reading about workable solutions affect your compassion fatigue?

GROUP DISCUSSION

- Did you choose a Bible passage to memorize this week? If so, what did you choose? What did you learn about yourself? If you didn't have a chance to memorize a Bible passage, what was an event or situation that dominated your week?

- Discuss your insights from the "Pre-Session Personal Study" questions. Your group leader will select the questions for discussion.

- What are one or two main insights you've had about the issues facing the poor and how to address them?

- How can you approach works of compassion and justice so that compassion fatigue doesn't paralyze you?

- Read "Living the Word" below. What is one opportunity that has been especially significant in your life?

- How can the group pray for you? For instance, do you need renewed hope and generosity to overcome compassion fatigue? Do you want God to point you to one area of need (clean water, malaria, one village, one child) rather than so many? Have someone in the group write down these things to pray for.

- Take time to pray for one another. Have someone in the group pray aloud from the list of requests while others pray silently. You may add prayers spontaneously if you wish. Close by saying together the Lord's Prayer:

  Our Father in heaven,
  hallowed be your name,
  your kingdom come,
  your will be done,
      on earth as it is in heaven.
  Give us today our daily bread.
  And forgive us our debts,
      as we also have forgiven our debtors.
  And lead us not into temptation,
      but deliver us from the evil one.
  For yours is the kingdom and the power
      and the glory forever. Amen.

PERSONAL ACTIVITY

LIVING THE WORD

Write down a list of opportunities and privileges you have had during your lifetime: education, clean water, health care, job opportunities, good nutrition, vaccinations, sanitation facilities, loans, and so forth. Circle one of these opportunities on your paper and spend some time praying for children and families who don't have it. Try to imagine what life is like for them. Ask God to give you his heart for them and to help you pray what he would have you pray for them.

When you're done, reflect on what it was like to pray for those children and families. Were you eager to pray? Did you find your mind wandering or your heart not wanting to connect with them? Do they feel close to you or far away? Would you rather keep them far away?

If it's hard for you to stay present with agonizing needs, try praying about solutions. Pray for the people who provide microfinance, or AIDS care, or malaria nets, or wells for clean water. Pray for renewed hope—for them and for yourself—knowing that what you do in the Lord is not in vain.

What opportunity did you choose?

What was it like for you to pray for children who need that opportunity?

AWOL

Whoever shuts their ears to the cry of the poor will also cry out
and not be answered.

Proverbs 21:13

OBJECTIVE

- To understand and reclaim the Church's role in addressing the needs of the global poor

- To explore what the Church has done and must do in this area

To prepare for this session, read chapters 15 through 18 of *The Hole in Our Gospel*. Meditate on the following quotes from the book and the Bible and answer the related questions.

> Can you see the problem? The American church in my little parable was not a "bad" church; it was just oblivious to the suffering of the church in Africa. It wasn't that they wouldn't help the African congregation; they were just so preoccupied with their own programs and people that they failed to see the bigger picture: the reality of the church across the world.
>
> There are some 350,000 individual congregations in the United States, which together possess unprecedented resources and capabilities. There are also hundreds of thousands of poor churches in the developing world, whose members struggle with daily survival. I try to imagine how this looks to God as he sees all of his churches—the wealthy and the needy—and wonders why the churches he has blessed have not reached out to their poor, burdened brothers and sisters. *(pp. 161–62)*

1. Is your local church preoccupied with its own programs and people? If so, to what extent is that a problem? Why?

And now, brothers and sisters, we want you to know about the grace that God has given the Macedonian churches. In the midst of a very severe trial, their overflowing joy and their extreme poverty welled up in rich generosity. For I testify that they gave as much as they were able, and even beyond their ability. Entirely on their own, they urgently pleaded with us for the privilege of sharing in this service to the Lord's people. . . .

But since you excel in everything—in faith, in speech, in knowledge, in complete earnestness and in the love we have kindled in you—see that you also excel in this grace of giving.

I am not commanding you, but I want to test the sincerity of your love by comparing it with the earnestness of others. For you know the grace of our Lord Jesus Christ, that though he was rich, yet for your sake he became poor, so that you through his poverty might become rich. . . .

Our desire is not that others might be relieved while you are hard pressed, but that there might be equality. . . . The goal is equality, as it is written: "The one who gathered much did not have too much, and the one who gathered little did not have too little." *(2 Corinthians 8:1–4, 7–9, 13–15)*

2. In the first paragraph of the above passage from 2 Corinthians, how does Paul say the poor Macedonian church responded to the needs of their poor fellow Christians in Jerusalem?

3. In the rest of the passage, Paul provides the prominent and wealthy Corinthian church additional reasons why they should be generous to the poor. What reasons does he give?

4. How is Paul's talk of "equality" different from socialism?

Listen to my Message,
    you Sodom-schooled leaders.
Receive God's revelation,
    you Gomorrah-schooled people.
"Why this frenzy of sacrifices?"
    GOD's asking.
"Don't you think I've had my fill of burnt sacrifices,
    rams and plump grain-fed calves?
Don't you think I've had my fill
    of blood from bulls, lambs, and goats?
When you come before me,
    whoever gave you the idea of acting like this,
Running here and there, doing this and that—
    all this sheer *commotion* in the place provided for worship?
Quit your worship charades.
    I can't stand your trivial religious games:
Monthly conferences, weekly Sabbaths, special meetings—
    meetings, meetings, meetings—I can't stand one more!

Meetings for this, meetings for that. I hate them!
    You've worn me out!
I'm sick of your religion, religion, religion,
    while you go right on sinning.
When you put on your next prayer-performance,
    I'll be looking the other way.
No matter how long or loud or often you pray,
    I'll not be listening.
And do you know why? Because you've been tearing
    people to pieces, and your hands are bloody.
Go home and wash up.
    Clean up your act.
Sweep your lives clean of your evildoings
    so I don't have to look at them any longer.
Say no to wrong.
    Learn to do good.
Work for justice.
    Help the down-and-out.
Stand up for the homeless.
    Go to bat for the defenseless." *(Isaiah 1:10–17 MSG)*

5. Do you think it's fair to quote this passage in Isaiah to American churches today? Why or why not? Which parts, if any, are relevant?

If we look at the things that God condemns when he looks at the behavior of his followers, once again it seems that sins of *omission* grieve him even more than sins of *commission*; yet it is these on which we tend to be fixated. Sins of commission occur when we do something to violate God's commands. These include murder, violence, theft, adultery, profanity, gossip, sexual promiscuity, exploiting the poor, among others. Most Christians and churches speak to these sins quite directly. In fact, our zeal to condemn these sins of commission often causes Christians to be perceived as judgmental and intolerant, always defined by what we are against rather than what we're for. But notice that God seems to get angrier about those things that he has commanded us but we have failed to do. Again, the book of James says it bluntly: "If anyone, then, knows the good they ought to do and doesn't do it, it is sin for them" (4:17). *(p. 169)*

6.   What do you think makes sins of omission so much harder or less popular to talk about than sins of commission?

I can remember distinctly the discomfort in the room as I brought together some of our marketing people and tried to marshal cooperation to raise both awareness and money in our donor community. There were awkward glances as I asked how we might take this issue out to our support base. Finally someone spoke up and said, "We're a G-rated ministry focused on children and families. AIDS is an R-rated issue. I don't think our donors are going to be willing to give for this, and if we push too hard, it could hurt our reputation." *(p. 177)*

7.   To what degree do you think the above comment from a World Vision employee helps to explain the Church's slowness to get into AIDS ministry? Do you think this is still a challenge today? Explain.

Perhaps every pastor, church leader, and parachurch ministry leader should begin their daily devotions with something similar to the Alcoholics Anonymous recitation as they pray that God would open their eyes to their own blind spots so they can lead their congregations through the strong currents of our secular culture. *My name is _____, and I am blind to the injustices and sins of omission committed by my own church. Open the eyes of my heart, Lord, to see the world as you see it. Let my heart be broken by the things that break your heart. Give me the ability to see through our culture and to lead my people with your vision, instead of the world's. (p. 180)*

8. What do you think would happen if pastors started praying the above prayer daily? Would good things happen? What resistance, if any, might they face from their congregations?

"No good tree bears bad fruit, nor does a bad tree bear good fruit. Each tree is recognized by its own fruit. . . ." (Luke 6:43–44). Therefore, faith and works should be seen not as two opposing ideas but as two manifestations of the same idea. A tree and its fruit are not different ideas in conflict with each other; rather, one is the natural product of the other. The tree is recognized by its fruit, and the fruit is produced inevitably by the tree. *(p. 182)*

9. How does your church talk about the relationship between faith and works? Do your leaders teach that good works are the natural fruit of a healthy and faith-filled tree? Explain.

In the early part of the twentieth century, a split in Christian theology resulted in a deep divide over the respective roles of faith and works. Liberals within the Church, as well as the wider society, began to attack historic, biblical Christianity. This liberal faction no longer saw the Church's mission as "saving souls" but rather, transforming society through humanitarianism—in other words, a social gospel based on *works*.

On the other side were those who staunchly defended a salvation by faith alone, offered only because of the *grace of God*, which they strongly emphasized. And because of a rise in premillennial eschatology, Christians in this group reasoned that since Jesus was coming back (and would cure all evil himself during his millennial reign), why bother trying to fix the world now? It was beyond redemption, riddled with evil, so the focus *ought* to be on saving souls for the *next* life. *(p. 183)*

10. In what ways has the split that occurred between liberal and conservative churches in the early twentieth century affected what your church teaches and practices?

And what about money? The American Dream often promotes this view of it: *I worked hard, I earned it, and it's mine to do with as I please.* This suggests that we are "entitled" to any income that comes to us because we worked for it. But that's not what the Bible tells us about our money and possessions. In fact, the biblical view of our resources is just the opposite. It teaches that all we have or receive comes from God; he has simply *entrusted* it to us. There's a big difference between *entitled* and *entrusted*.

Listen to what Moses told the nation of Israel just before they entered the promised land. Note especially God's view of the source of prosperity.

> When you have eaten and are satisfied, praise the LORD your God for the good land he has given you. Be careful that you do not forget the LORD your God. . . . Otherwise, when you eat and are satisfied, when you build fine houses and settle down, and when your herds and flocks grow large and your silver and gold increase and all you have is multiplied, then your heart will become proud and you will forget the LORD your God, who brought you out of Egypt, out of the land of slavery. He led you through the vast and dreadful desert, that thirsty and waterless land, with its venomous snakes and scorpions. He brought you water out of hard rock. He gave you manna to eat in the desert, something your fathers had never known. . . . You may say to yourself, "My power and the strength of my hands have produced this wealth for me." But remember the LORD your God, for it is he who gives you the ability to produce wealth. . . . (Deuteronomy 8:10–18 NIV 1984) *(p. 187)*

11. Do you tend to think and act as though your power and the strength of your hands have produced your wealth? Or do you tend to think and act as though God has entrusted everything that you have received? What actions show that tendency?

Three clear principles, then, differentiate the scriptural view of money from the American Dream view:

   1. It is not our money—it all comes from God.
   2. We are not *entitled* to it but *entrusted with* it.
   3. God expects us to use it in the interest of his kingdom. . . .

   How about you? How do you look at your assets (car, bank accounts, home)? What about your giftings? Are you *entitled* to them to do with as you please, or were they *entrusted* to you for a purpose—God's purpose? *(p. 190)*

12. What would happen if your church taught the scriptural view of money described above? Or, if your church does teach this, how does (or doesn't) that affect the way individuals and the congregation as a whole use the money entrusted to them?

GROUP DISCUSSION

- What happened this week when you prayed for children who do not have the same opportunities and privileges that you have? If you didn't have a chance to do this, what was an event or situation that dominated your week?

- Discuss your insights from the "Pre-Session Personal Study" questions. Your group leader will select the questions for discussion.

- What role do you think your church should play in addressing global poverty?

- What challenges will your church face in doing that—challenges from the congregation, the leadership, financial limitations, and so forth?

- Read "Living the Word" below. Do you have any idea yet what steps your group might take?

- Today, instead of praying for each person individually, pray for your small group and for your church. Confess and ask God to forgive your sins of omission. Pray for your leaders, who are no doubt dealing with numerous needs and vast expectations. Pray for those who make decisions about how money is spent. Ask God how you can be a positive influence in your church. Close by saying together the Lord's Prayer:

Our Father in heaven,
hallowed be your name,
your kingdom come,
your will be done,
    on earth as it is in heaven.
Give us today our daily bread.
And forgive us our debts,
    as we also have forgiven our debtors.
And lead us not into temptation,
    but deliver us from the evil one.
For yours is the kingdom and the power
    and the glory forever. Amen.

LIVING THE WORD

In session 5, you're going to look at some churches that are making a difference. As you do, keep in mind this question: "What could my church do?" Pray about that question. The answer might begin with action your small group could take, so pray about this question as well: "What could my small group do?" Write down any ideas that come to you. This need not involve reinventing wheels—you could connect with or raise funds for an organization that is already reaching out to the poor.

If the challenges your group or church face loom large in your mind, write those down and ask God to help you address the challenges.

What could your church do?

What could your small group do?

What challenges might you face?

WHAT IF?

How different our standard is from Christ's. We ask how much a man gives. He asks how much he keeps.

Andrew Murray

OBJECTIVES

- To learn about congregations and communities that have been transformed by the bigger vision of the gospel and the kingdom of God

- To begin considering how your small group or your church could participate in the larger work of the kingdom

To prepare for this session, read chapters 19 through 22 of *The Hole in Our Gospel.* Meditate on the following quotes from the book and the Bible and answer the related questions.

> According to the book of Leviticus, the first 10 percent of our income is to be offered to God: "A tithe of everything from the land, whether grain from the soil or fruit from the trees, belongs to the LORD; it is holy to the LORD" (27:30). The tithe was not considered a gift to God—it *belonged* to God. There were other provisions that spoke to freewill giving, but any such offerings were to be over and above the 10 percent required for the tithe. That first 10 percent was seen as a bare minimum one would set aside for the Lord. *(pp. 193–94)*

1. How do you respond to the idea of making 10 percent the bare minimum of what you set aside for the Lord? Is this difficult for you to do? Why or why not?

It is important to put the American Church in perspective. Simply stated, it is the wealthiest community of Christians in the history of Christendom. How wealthy? The total income of American churchgoers is about $6.5 trillion. (That's six and a half thousand billion dollars.) It would take just a little over 1 percent of the income of American Christians to lift the poorest one billion people in the world out of extreme poverty. Said another way, American Christians, who make up about 5 percent of the Church worldwide, control about half of global Christian wealth; a lack of money is not our problem. *(p. 199)*

2. Calculate 1 percent of your family's annual income. (You won't have to share the exact number with your group.) How does that look as an annual sum to spend to help lift a billion people out of extreme poverty? What about 5 percent?

Imagine how stunning it would be to the watching world for American Christians to give so generously that it:

- brought an end to world hunger;

- solved the clean water crisis;

- provided universal access to drugs and medical care for the millions suffering from AIDS, malaria, and tuberculosis;

- virtually eliminated eighteen thousand daily child deaths;

- guaranteed education for all the world's children;

- provided a safety net for the world's tens of millions of orphans.

Think about the statement it would make if American Christian citizens stepped up and gave more than all of the governments of the world combined because they took Jesus seriously when he said to love our neighbors as ourselves. Terrorists might have a harder time recruiting young men to attack a nation so compassionate. Other wealthy nations might be shamed— or inspired to follow our example. Adherents of other religions would surely wonder what motivates the Christians to be so loving and generous. *(p. 201)*

3. Do you think these effects might actually happen if American Christians stepped up and became that generous with the money with which they've been entrusted? Explain what you think could happen.

In 1999, Pastor John Thomas heard a shocking statistic at a local minister's meeting. Forty-four percent of the population of Masiphumelele, a shantytown slum community of black migrants embedded near the tiny seaside town of Fish Hoek, South Africa, were HIV-positive. This high percentage stunned Pastor Thomas, whose predominantly white church of about 315 members had little awareness of the impact of AIDS in their own backyard. Just five years after the end of apartheid, relations between black and white were still strained in South Africa, a country that now had more HIV infections than any nation in the world. Thomas was provoked. *How can I face God on judgment day*, he thought, *realizing I've done nothing about the greatest problem that lies on our doorstep?*

The troubled pastor decided to share his heart with his church—and nothing has been the same since. Fish Hoek Baptist Church is now known around town as "the church that cares." Almost ten years later, the AIDS ministry of Fish Hoek Baptist Church, known as Living Hope, had a budget of $1.2 million a year and a full-time staff of 147. By comparison, the church's annual budget was just $300,000 with a staff of 10. The AIDS ministry dwarfed the church in size and scope. . . .

Living Hope encompasses virtually every dimension of the impact of AIDS in the lives of the poor. A sister church has been established in the heart of Masiphumelele to provide a permanent and accessible spiritual presence for the community. A twenty-bed clinic, Living Hope Health Care Centre, for treating the gravest cases of AIDS has been built and staffed with a full complement of health-care workers and counselors. Alongside the center is the Living Way ministry, where HIV support groups can meet and men and women can receive training in job skills so they can support themselves economically after leaving the clinic. Because the patients are receiving antiretroviral drug therapy, most of them recover and reenter their communities.

("Charity has its place," said one of the staff, "but it's not sustainable.") Across the street is a retail store that sells some of the crafts and jewelry made by the women from Living Hope. *(pp. 213–14)*

4. How is Fish Hoek Baptist Church similar to the church you attend?

5. How is it different?

6. What thought prompted Pastor John Thomas to drastically change what Fish Hoek was doing in response to the AIDS crisis?

7. The budget for Fish Hoek's Living Hope ministry trumps the church's overall budget. What does this say about their priorities? How does your own church's budget compare in terms of money spent on outreach versus money spent on the facilities and staff?

Pastor Thomas was honest about the struggles they have faced. Some in the church were not as enthusiastic about his vision, and there were divisions, often leading him to wonder whether he would be able to keep his job. There was also what he called "AIDS fatigue"; it isn't easy to face the bleakness of AIDS and poverty every single day. This weary pastor acknowledges that this is a constant struggle and that it has been difficult to get other churches involved. Why? "This is not the prosperity gospel," he says.

Thankfully, Living Hope has seven volunteer missionaries from the United States and Canada, and about eight US churches partner with them consistently, sending additional volunteers. *(p. 216)*

8. Can you imagine your church partnering with another church or a Christian organization that is doing this kind of work in the developing world? Why or why not? What would it take to make that happen?

Christian Family Church, started in the 1970s, found itself besieged by the growing AIDS pandemic in the 1980s and '90s. With shame in his voice, Pastor Morgan Chilulu told me, "We looked at being HIV-positive as negative. We related HIV to sin. We would say people were not living right with God. Our church pushed people away." But in 2003, World Vision invited Chilulu and thirty other pastors to a workshop to help African churches cope with the impact of AIDS on their communities. "It had a very big impact," he said. "The Bible says, 'Do not judge.' We were driving people away from God. Now we are winning people back." The workshop was a wake-up call to Pastor Chilulu, and it transformed his vision for Christian Family Church. "Now our vision is to empower believers. This church has 120 members, but we are a megachurch," he told me.

How did he transform his biased congregation? First, he had to deal with the stigma that surrounded HIV and AIDS. He challenged his flock to see people through God's eyes. The church began to organize six-member "Hope Teams" to serve people affected by AIDS. One of the Hope Team members said, "Before when I saw people who were infected, I thought, *Just let them be like that*. Now I know that we are just the same. Even if I am not infected, I am affected. I have compassion for them now. I am a different person." And the church is now a different church. Hope Teams go out into the community to visit and care for widows and orphans. The weekly rounds are organized such that no one is left out. The church prepares meals for the sick and the orphans and offers counseling as well. . . .

Milton . . . an orphan . . . understands hopelessness. But now, filled with enthusiasm for his work, he said, "We want to leave a legacy. When we die, we hope what we did is remembered." *(pp. 217–18)*

9. Do you think members of your congregation look down on the poor or on AIDS victims? If so, what could you or your small group do to help the church overcome that attitude?

FIND TREASURE IN TRASH. Fund-raising ideas can come from anywhere. Tara Paul of San Diego had a "duh!" moment when her twelve-year-old daughter wrote an essay suggesting that funds from recycling bottles and cans be used for worthy causes. So Tara started a ministry called DUH—Desperate, Underprivileged, and Hungry—and organized her church, The Rock, to bring their bottles and cans in with them each Sunday. The ministry raises about $4,500 monthly and currently sponsors one hundred children. Not only do they collect at church; they are proactive in supporting and collecting at other Rock community outreach events. *(p. 285)*

TAX YOURSELF FOR LITTLE LUXURIES. This is an ingenious idea from The Journey Church in San Jose, California, a congregation of 225. The church printed Luxury Tax cards based on the board game Monopoly and asked members to tax themselves based on luxuries they take for granted, such as the number of water taps or toilets in their homes. They've raised more than $25,000 for Limpopo, an AIDS-devastated community in Zimbabwe. *(p. 285)*

DONATE A DAY'S WAGES. Whether your daily wages amount to a big number or a small one, anyone with a job can do this. Eugene and Minhee Cho, a pastor and his wife in Seattle, invited their family, friends, and the rest of the world to donate one day's wages and to renew that pledge every year on their birthdays. For this they created the website onedayswages.org, which includes information on global poverty and a handy wage calculator. Using the power of the Internet and social media, they've garnered nearly eight hundred thousand fans on Facebook. *(p. 286)*

10. Consider the three fund-raising ideas at the three American churches described here. What fund-raising idea might work in your church?

When historians look back in one hundred years, what will they write about this nation of 350,000 churches? What will they say of the Church's response to the great challenges of our time—AIDS, poverty, hunger, terrorism, war? Will they say that these authentic Christians rose up courageously and responded to the tide of human suffering, that they rushed to the front lines to comfort the afflicted and to douse the flames of hatred? Will they write of an unprecedented outpouring of generosity to meet the urgent needs of the world's poor? Will they speak of the moral leadership and compelling vision of our leaders? Will they write that this, the beginning of the twenty-first century, was the Church's finest hour?

Or will they look back and see a Church too comfortable, insulated from the pain of the rest of the world, empty of compassion, and devoid of deeds? *(p. 220)*

11. Have the examples of the churches in this session inspired you to do anything differently? If so, what have they inspired you to do?

GROUP DISCUSSION

- Did you have any ideas this week about what your church or small group could do to serve the needs of the poor or change attitudes in your church? If the challenges of action still loom large for you, what do you see as the major obstacles?

- Discuss your insights from the "Pre-Session Personal Study" questions. Your group leader will select the questions for discussion. Note that it's not necessary to share personal information about your financial decisions.

- Read "Living the Word" below. When you think about evaluating what you really have to give, what is one area of resistance or obstacle in your life that you will have to confront?

- Pray for your church and your small group. Ask God to show you what your group can do to set an example for your church, or to educate your church, or to raise funds. Talk with God about the challenges you face in taking action and influencing the priorities at your church. Pray for your leaders. Ask for discernment, creativity, and courage.

- Pray for one another. In your preparation for session 6, you're going to evaluate your individual time, talent, and treasure. Some in your group may be deeply conscious of time pressure, limited finances, and limited skills, so ask God to show each person in the group what he or she has to offer. Pray about the obstacles or areas of resistance you have identified. Ask for insight and boldness. Close by saying together the Lord's Prayer:

> Our Father in heaven,
> hallowed be your name,
> your kingdom come,
> your will be done,
>   on earth as it is in heaven.
> Give us today our daily bread.
> And forgive us our debts,
>   as we also have forgiven our debtors.
> And lead us not into temptation,
>   but deliver us from the evil one.
> For yours is the kingdom and the power
>   and the glory forever. Amen.

PERSONAL ACTIVITY

LIVING THE WORD

As mentioned above, in the next session you will evaluate the time, talents (abilities, skills, and gifts), and treasure (money) you can devote to works of compassion and justice. You may be fired up to take action and eager to assess what you can do, or you may be reluctant because of your busyness, your limitations, or your financial responsibilities. So, before you begin your preparation for session 6, take time to pray, offering any questions or areas of reluctance to God. Be honest with him—he can take it. Ask him to stretch you and show you what is truly possible.

WHAT ARE YOU GOING TO DO ABOUT IT?

Vision without action is merely a dream. Action without vision just passes the time. Vision with action can change the world.

Joel Barker

OBJECTIVES

- To identify specific ways we can engage with God's kingdom mission of justice and compassion

- To deal with lingering reasons for resisting God's call

PRE-SESSION PERSONAL STUDY

To prepare for this session, please read chapters 23 through 26 of *The Hole in Our Gospel*, Appendix 2 (pp. 273–288) and Appendix 3 (pp. 293–304).

> The difference between the pre- and post-resurrection disciples was astonishing.
>
> > Fear became courage;
> > > timidity became boldness;
> > > > uncertainty became confidence
>
> as their lives were given over to the revolution that the gospel—the good news—envisioned. Everything changed because *they* had been changed, and they had been changed because Christ had risen. *(p. 226)*

1. What have you read and experienced in this study that has helped you move toward courage, confidence, and boldness?

2. What fears or uncertainty do you still have?

3. Will those fears or uncertainties stop you from taking action? Why or why not?

One of the most common mistakes we can make is to believe that we have nothing of significance to offer—that we're not rich enough, smart enough, skilled enough, or spiritual enough to make much difference at all, especially in the face of huge global problems. . . . But the very good news for those of us who want to follow Christ and be part of God's plan for our world is that he uses what we have to offer, no matter how unimportant we think it might be. *(p. 233)*

The apostles gathered around Jesus and reported to him all they had done and taught. Then, because so many people were coming and going that they did not even have a chance to eat, he said to them, "Come with me by yourselves to a quiet place and get some rest."

So they went away by themselves in a boat to a solitary place. But many who saw them leaving recognized them and ran on foot from all the towns and got there ahead of them. When Jesus landed and saw a large crowd, he had compassion on them, because they were like sheep without a shepherd. So he began teaching them many things.

By this time it was late in the day, so his disciples came to him. "This is a remote place," they said, "and it's already very late. Send the people away so that they can go to the surrounding countryside and villages and buy themselves something to eat."

But he answered, "You give them something to eat."

They said to him, "That would take more than half a year's wages! Are we to go and spend that much on bread and give it to them to eat?"

"How many loaves do you have?" he asked. "Go and see."

When they found out, they said, "Five—and two fish."

Then Jesus directed them to have all the people sit down in groups on the green grass. So they sat down in groups of hundreds and fifties. Taking the five loaves and the two fish and looking up to heaven, he gave thanks and broke the loaves. Then he gave them to his disciples to distribute to the people. He also divided the two fish among them all. They all ate and were satisfied, and the disciples picked up twelve basketfuls of broken pieces of bread and fish. The number of the men who had eaten was five thousand. *(Mark 6:30–44)*

4. According to this passage in Mark, what problems did the disciples see? What was Jesus' solution?

5. Imagine Jesus saying to you, "How many loaves do you have? Go and see" (v. 38). Imagine him asking you what you have to give. What is your reply?

Nehemiah was not willing to accept the status quo. He had a different vision. After weeping and fasting, Nehemiah prayed, first asking forgiveness for himself and the apathy and sin of God's people. Then he challenged the Jews of Jerusalem to act: "You see the trouble we are in: Jerusalem lies in ruins, and its gates have been burned with fire. Come, let us rebuild the wall of Jerusalem, and we will no longer be in disgrace" (2:17). *(p. 237)*

6. Nehemiah was a man of prayer, vision, and action. What role will prayer have in your response to global poverty? For instance, you can:

    • Adopt the seven steps toward integrating prayer for the poor into your life (pp. 280–81). Consider taking on this practice for a month or forty days.

    • Put the Franciscan benediction (p. 281) on a card where you'll see it daily.

- Pray daily regarding some specific need that is on your heart.

- Seek God's voice about what action he wants you to take.

- Other (name it):

7. On pages 282–288 in *The Hole in Our Gospel*, there are several ideas listed for taking action. Read those ideas, and then put checkmarks beside any of the items below that give you some ideas for things you might do:

❏ Sponsor a child

❏ Volunteer in your own city or town

❏ Take on a service project with your small group

❏ Hold a "Hope Sunday" at your church to encourage people to sponsor children

❏ Take a short-term mission trip or learning trip

❏ Do your professional work pro bono in a developing country

❏ Raise funds for your favorite charity

❏ Run a marathon, climb a mountain, or do some other activity to raise awareness and funds for the poor

- ❏ Carry child sponsorship information with you wherever you go, and talk to people about it

- ❏ Organize and package supplies, such as Caregiver Kits or SchoolTools, to send overseas

- ❏ Set a new financial giving goal

- ❏ Designate your favorite charity in your will

- ❏ Find out if your company matches charitable donations

- ❏ Collect recyclables and donate the funds raised to a charity

- ❏ Auction your time and skills and donate the funds raised

- ❏ Tax yourself for little luxuries and donate the funds raised

- ❏ Give meaningful gifts through alternate-giving catalogs

- ❏ Give to the poor as much as you spend on your pets

- ❏ Write to Congress to support legislation for alleviating global poverty

- ❏ Organize an in-district meeting for your elected officials to discuss issues facing the poor

- ❏ Use social media to spread the word about your cause

- ❏ Join an advocacy group

- ❏ Other (name it):

Let's say that each of us on average has about two hours each day that might be available for service if we so chose. Over the course of the year, if we valued our time at just $10 an hour, that would be the equivalent of more than $7,000 that each of us could make available for ministry. *(p. 242)*

8.   Take a look at your schedule and see if you can make any space in it to give time to God's call. Be creative.

    For example, think about the time you spend watching TV, surfing the Internet, or enhancing your personal appearance. Can any of that time be used differently? Can any of the time you spend with your children be devoted to spending time *with your children while serving people* outside your family? Might that time be well spent in showing them what matters in life? Or, if your career is a 24/7 commitment, is that because you look to it for self-worth?

    The time might be used for something as simple as listening to someone or spending quality time with someone to let them know they are important. It might be given to a volunteer opportunity such as tutoring students, becoming an advocate for a child in the court system, or doing your professional work pro bono.

Let's start with your unique personality and character traits. Are you outgoing, contemplative, determined, stubborn, visionary, thoughtful, funny? All of those parts of you describe how God uniquely made you. They are also characteristics that God intends to use in your service to him. Your *talents* also include your life experiences. Each of us has a unique life history, made up of our family background, education, professional and work history, experiences and the wisdom gained from them, relationships, and connections. No one has ever lived the same life as you, and that is one of the things that makes your "puzzle piece" extraordinary. We also have interests and passions that God has placed in our hearts. . . . You may be fascinated by politics or passionate about running marathons. But whatever your objects of deepest interest, they may provide clues to your particular way of serving. *(p. 245)*

9. Make a list of your personality and character traits. If you don't know what they are, ask your spouse or a friend.

10. Make a list of some of your life experiences that help to equip you to offer something to the world. What have you experienced that has made you a little wiser or more skilled in some way?

11. What are your interests and your passions?

Austin Gutwein was just nine when he learned about children in Africa who had become orphaned because of AIDS. Most adults would laugh at the idea of a nine-year-old tackling the global AIDS pandemic, but Austin believed he could do something—that he had a "talent" that God could use. . . . Today Austin has thousands of kids in two hundred different locations doing Hoops of Hope in most of the fifty states and in other countries around the world. His cumulative fund-raising is approaching one million dollars. Think of it: a million bucks—for *shooting hoops! (p. 247–48)*

12. How does the story of Austin Gutwein and Hoops for Hope affect you? What does it tell you about who God can use to tackle the issues of the world today?

It doesn't take billions of dollars to make a difference. The lack of clean water causes millions of needless child deaths each year. Yet the cost to bring clean water to one person costs only *one dollar per year*! When you realize that a gift as small as a dollar can save a life, it is hard to argue that you're not wealthy enough to make a difference. *(p. 249)*

13. How much money per month or per year can you contribute to global justice and compassion? (Note that you won't have to share this figure with your group.)

14. What sense do you currently have, if any, of what you might do with that money? If you don't know, what are you passionate about? What steps can you take to choose an organization that would use your funds wisely?

GROUP DISCUSSION

- What was it like for you to evaluate your time, talents, and treasure? Which one of those was easiest for you? Which was hardest?

- Discuss your insights from the "Pre-Session Personal Study" questions. Your group leader will select the questions for discussion. It's not necessary to share details of your financial decisions.

- Read "Living the Word" below. What is one thing you are committed to doing? Talk about your individual commitments, and then talk about what you can do as a group.

- In your prayer time, thank God for specific things he has done through this small-group experience. Thank him for things you've learned, ways you've changed, and ideas you've had. Thank him for the time, talents, and treasure he has given each person. Think of specific things that others in the group have offered and thank him for those gifts. Ask him to multiply your resources so that you can follow through on the things you have committed to doing. Close by saying together the Lord's Prayer:

  Our Father in heaven,
  hallowed be your name,
  your kingdom come,
  your will be done,
      on earth as it is in heaven.
  Give us today our daily bread.
  And forgive us our debts,
      as we also have forgiven our debtors.
  And lead us not into temptation,
      but deliver us from the evil one.
  For yours is the kingdom and the power
      and the glory forever. Amen.

LIVING THE WORD

What is one thing you are committed to doing with your time, talents, and/or treasure on behalf of the world's poor? What are you committed to doing on your own or with your family? What are you committed to doing with your small group and/or your church?

Break up your plan into steps that need to be completed. If necessary, lay out a timeline by which you will complete these steps. Whose help, if any, do you need?

GROUP LEADER NOTES

T hank you for giving of your time and talent to lead a group study of *The Hole in Our Gospel*. This will be a six-session experience built around weekly small-group gatherings (or however often your group meets together).

As group leader, imagine yourself as the host of a dinner party whose job is to manage all the behind-the-scenes details so your guests can focus on each other and interact around the topic. You need not answer all the questions—in fact, you should spend more time listening than talking (and never send the message that you will answer the questions if others are silent). You need not teach the content (the book does that). This will make your small group more of a learning community—a place to process, question, and reflect on what the author, Rich Stearns, is teaching.

Make sure everyone in the group gets a copy of the study guide. Encourage the group members to write in their guides and bring the book with them every week. This will keep everyone on the same page and help the session run more smoothly.

Likewise, encourage every participant (or every couple) to get a copy of *The Hole in Our Gospel* so they can complete the pre-session personal preparation before the group meets each week. If some participants can't obtain copies, see if anyone from the group is willing to donate an extra copy or two for sharing. Giving everyone access to all the material will help this study be as rewarding as possible.

PREPARATION

If you are leading a group study, you will need to do the following to prepare for each session:

- Read the relevant chapters of *The Hole in Our Gospel*.

- Write your own answers to the pre-session questions.

- If your group discussion time is limited, select those pre-session questions that you definitely want to discuss with the group. You might put stars by six or seven questions that you definitely want to discuss. Then, depending on how talkative the group is, you can add additional questions during the meeting.

- Think about your own response to the "Living the Word" section.

- Pray for your group.

HOSPITALITY

As group leader, you will want to create an environment that is conducive to sharing and learning. (Note that a church sanctuary or classroom may not be ideal for this kind of meeting, as they can feel formal and less intimate.) Whatever venue you choose, make sure there is enough comfortable seating for everyone and, if possible, arrange the chairs in a circle.

Try to get to the meeting site early so you can greet participants as they arrive, especially newcomers. Simple refreshments can create a welcoming atmosphere and be a wonderful addition to a group-study gathering. If you do serve food, try to take into account any food allergies or dietary restrictions group members may have. Also, if you meet in a home, find out if the house has pets (in case there are any allergies) and even consider offering childcare to couples with children who want to attend.

LEADING YOUR GROUP

Once everyone has arrived, it is time to begin the group. If you are new to small-group leadership, what follows are some simple tips to making your group time healthy, enjoyable, and effective.

First, consider beginning the meeting with prayer. Remind people to silence and put away their mobile phones. This is a way to say yes to being present to each other and to God.

Follow the outline in the "Group Discussion" section. The first question in session 1 is an ice-breaker. Allow everyone in the group to have a chance to answer it, though it is okay for participants to pass if they wish. Beginning with session 2, the first question will be a check-in related to the "Living the Word" exercise.

Next, discuss the pre-session questions. Note that it's not a good idea to go around the circle and have everyone answer every one of these questions—a free-flowing discussion is more desirable. Encourage group members to talk to each other, not to you. As the discussion progresses, follow up with comments such as, "Tell me more about that," or, "Can you talk about your reasons for answering the way you did?" This will allow participants to deepen their reflections, and it will invite meaningful sharing in a nonthreatening way. You can bring others into the conversation by asking, "What do others think?" or, "Did anyone have a different response?"

It is not necessary to discuss every question if you're having a fruitful conversation, but do move the group along if the discussion bogs down or goes off on a tangent. It's also not necessary to discuss the questions in numerical order. You can discuss your top half-dozen first, and then go back to those you skipped. Or you can move to a question that addresses something that has come up in the discussion.

Many of the pre-session questions are personal. At times people may prefer not to share their answers, and they need not do so. (This is another good reason for not going around the circle.)

Don't be afraid of silence. Offering a question and allowing up to thirty seconds of silence gives people space to think about how they want to respond. Resist the urge to answer questions yourself to fill the void.

You are the boundary keeper for your group. So don't let anyone (yourself included) dominate the discussion. Keep an eye out for group members who might be tempted to attack people they disagree with or who try to "fix" those having struggles. Such behaviors can derail a group's momentum. Model active listening and encourage everyone in the group to do the same. This will make your group time a safe space and foster the kind of community that God can use to change people.

During your discussion, you may sometimes find it helpful to have someone read aloud the excerpts from the book. Be sure to read aloud the Bible passages before you discuss them. Save time at the end to look at the "Living the Word" section together, and ask how you can pray for group members.

End your time together in prayer. Some ideas for prayer are suggested in each session, but feel free to strike out on your own. Some groups are comfortable praying extemporaneously, while others are not used to praying aloud in front of others. Just make sure you do something intentional to mark the conclusion of the meeting.

ABOUT WORLD VISION

Who we are

World Vision is a Christian humanitarian organization dedicated to working with children, families, and their communities worldwide to reach their full potential by tackling the causes of poverty and injustice.

World Vision has more than 1,300 staff in the United States, and partners with U.S. government agencies, corporations, foundations, churches, and more than 1.1 million individual donors to help children and their communities overcome poverty and experience "fullness of life," as described in John 10:10. It is the largest member of the global World Vision Partnership, which works in nearly 100 countries through 45,000 staff (around 95 percent of whom are local).

Whom we serve

Motivated by faith in Jesus Christ, World Vision staff serve alongside the poor and oppressed as a demonstration of God's unconditional love for all people. World Vision serves all people, regardless of religion, race, ethnicity, or gender.

How we serve

World Vision has more than 60 years of experience in serving the poor, and works in three key areas—emergency relief, long-term development, and advocacy—to help children and families thrive. In each community where it works, the organization leverages its broad skills and expertise along with its extensive network of global and local partnerships, enabling World Vision to effectively support children's physical, social, emotional, and spiritual well-being.

For more information, go to **worldvision.org.**

> ### You can help:
>
> Want to put your faith into action? Become a World Vision child sponsor and build a friendship with one special child who will know your name, write to you, and feel your love and prayers. Your monthly sponsorship gift will help provide a child and their family and community with sustainable access to life-changing essentials like clean water, nutritious food, healthcare, educational opportunities, and spiritual nurture.
>
> Become a sponsor today at **worldvision.org/sponsorship**

PRESI35819_0313 © 2013 World Vision, Inc.

At the author's request, all royalties due to the author will benefit World Vision's work with children in need.

BELIEVING
IS ONLY THE BEGINNING

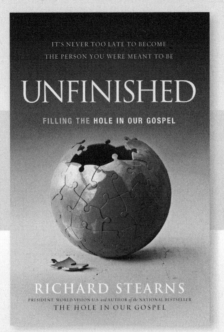

So you believe in God. Now what? What is our purpose and where do we fit in the bigger story that God is writing? How should faith affect our families, our careers, and our money? Why does it all matter? In *Unfinished*, Rich Stearns takes us on a breathtaking journey to rediscover the critical mission of Christ in our world today and the richness of God's calling on our lives.